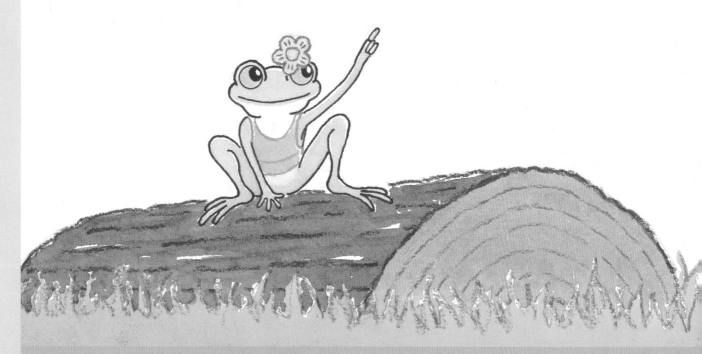

One butterfly is flying.

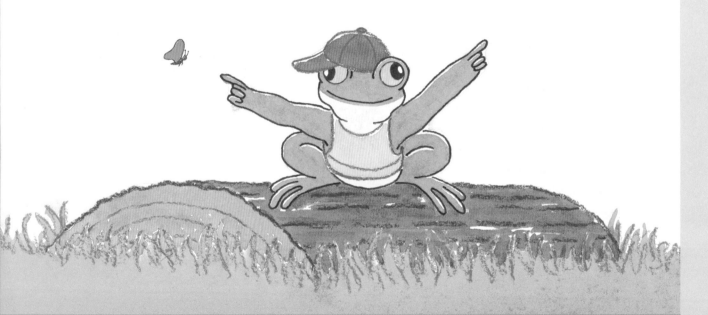

Two butterflies are flying.

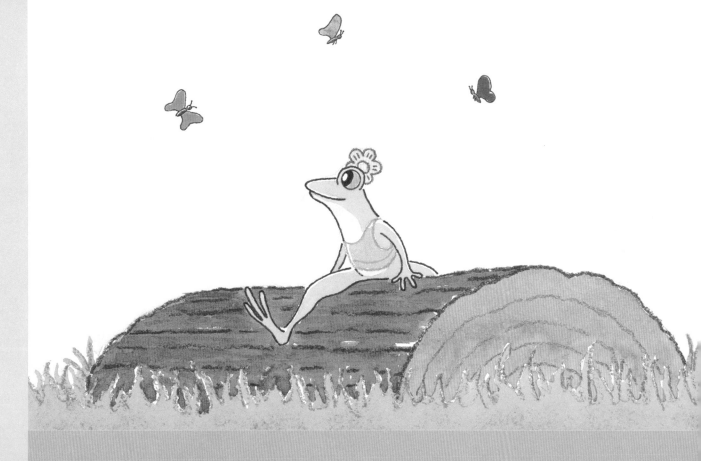

Three butterflies are flying.

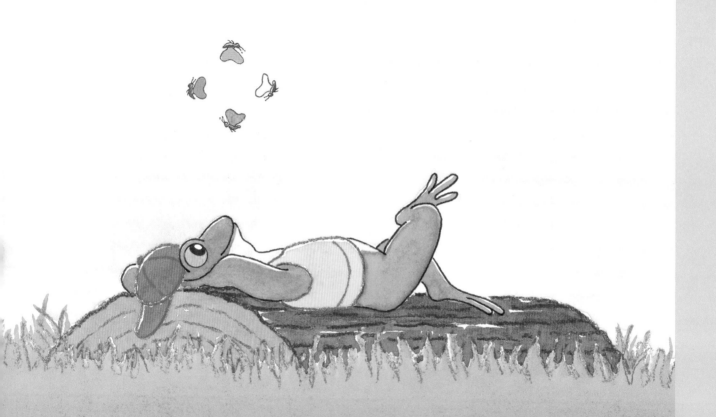

Four butterflies are flying.

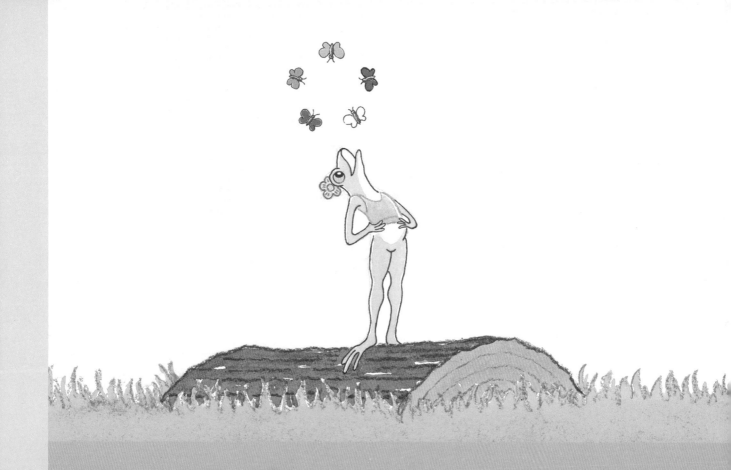

Five butterflies are flying.

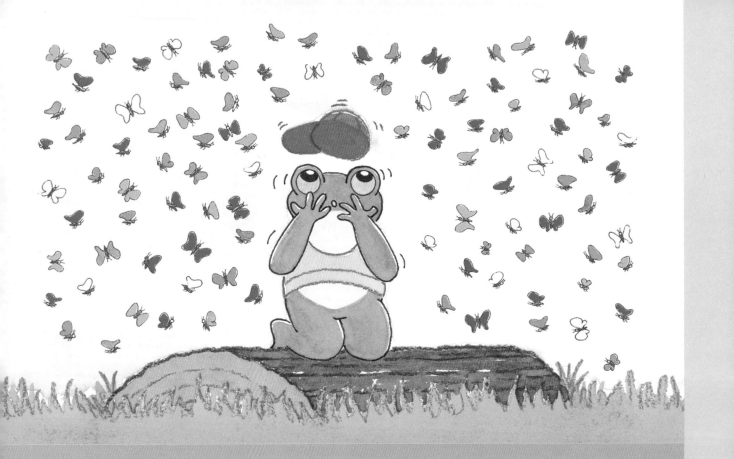

One hundred butterflies are flying.

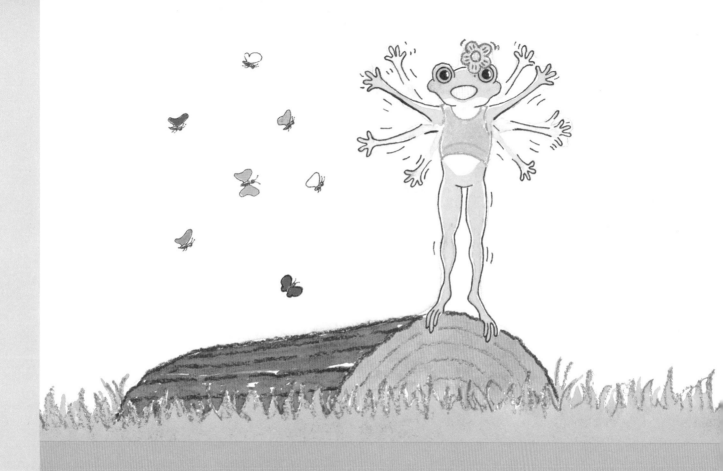

"Look at me fly," says Lucy.

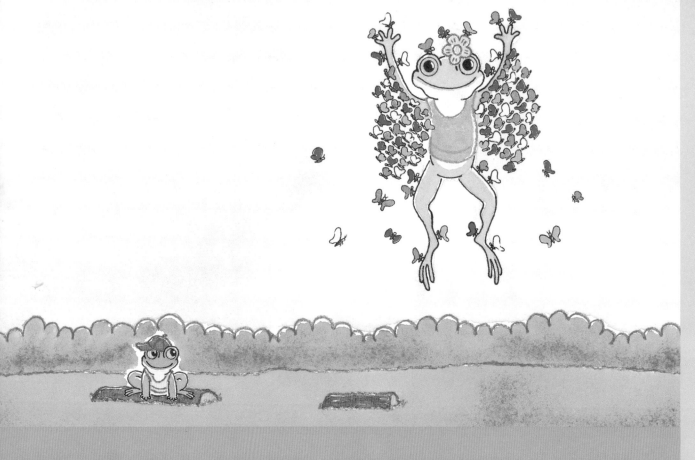

"Look at me fly!"